Written by Elizabeth Newlove

I am going to see my gran.
She has a flat in a big town.

I travel there on the train.
I go with my dad.

I like to chat to my gran and grandad on the laptop.

They clap when I do handstands!

I go with my twin sister to see
Gran down the street. It is not far.

We cross one road and Gran greets us at her coffee shop.

My dad and I are on the bus.
We are going out to meet Grandad
at the park.

We stop for a sandwich and a drink.
Then I have a go on the swing.

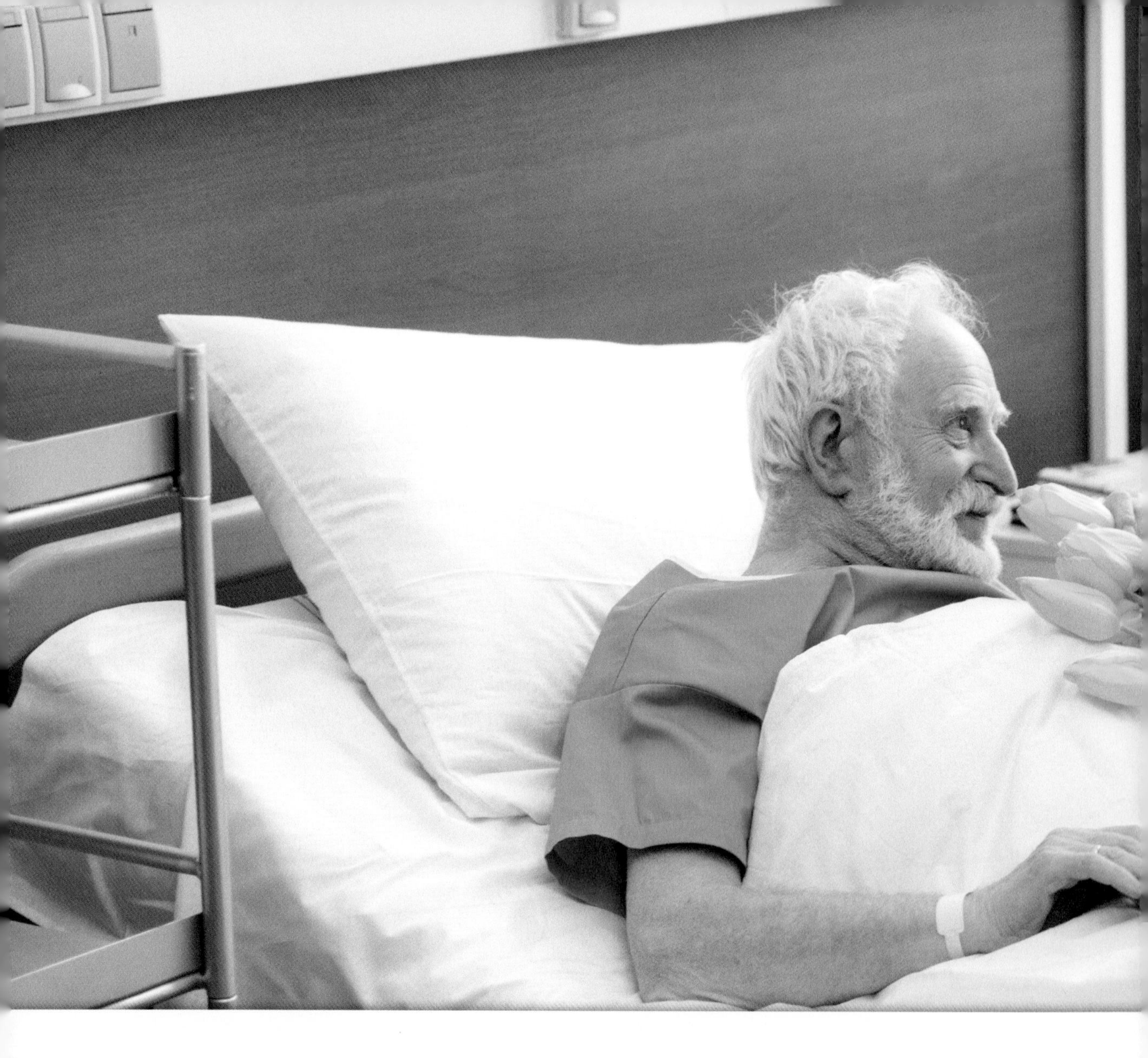

I am visiting my grandad in
hospital. I have a gift for him.

When he is better, I will visit him at his flat and help him.

I visit my nana on her farm.
I feed the chickens corn.

She has a pond and we like to spot the frogs swimming.

My grandad likes to travel with his little tent.

He sleeps under the starlight and sends me letters with cool stamps.

Grans and grandads are the best!